First published in 1990 by Usborne Publishing Ltd.
Usborne House, 83–85 Saffron Hill, London EC1N 8RT.

Illustrations copyright © 1990 Stephen Cartwright
Text copyright © 1990 Heather Amery.

The name Usborne and the device ♟
are Trade Marks of Usborne Publishing Ltd.

Printed in Great Britain.
This edition published in 1997 by Tiger Books International PLC, Twickenham
ISBN 1-85501-879-9

# THE STEPHEN CARTWRIGHT
# ABC
## Heather Amery & Stephen Cartwright

**TIGER BOOKS INTERNATIONAL**
**LONDON**

A                                                                    a

a                                                                    A

# Aa

A is for Alex, Andrew and Anne
Who gave an apple to their old gran.

# Bb

B is for Betty, Billy and Bret
Who bought a butterfly as a pet.

# Cc

C is for Corinne, Chris and Carol
Who caught a crocodile in a barrel.

# Dd

D is for Daisy, Daniel and Dave
Who dragged a dinosaur from its cave.

# Ee

E is for Emily, Ed and Elaine
Who washed an elephant in the rain.

# Ff

F is for Fanny, Felix and Fred
Who hid from fireworks under the bed.

# Gg

G is for Gordon, Gertie and Greg
Who gave a gorilla a golden egg.

# Hh

H is for Helen, Henry and Hank
Whose house is on a green river bank.

# K k

K is for Katie, Kaspar and Koo
Who ran away with a kangaroo.

# L l

L is for Leo, Lucy and Lynn
Who tickled a lion under its chin.

# Mm

M is for Martin, Maggie and Mark
Who sat with a monster in the dark.

# Nn

N is for Nancy, Nicky and Ned
Who found a nest all made out of bread.

# Oo

O is for Olive, Oscar, Odette
Who caught an ostrich in a net.

# Pp

P is for Peter, Polly and Pat
Who played with a pig in a big pink hat.

# Qq

Q is for Quentin, Quincy and Quin
Who had tea with a queen, tall and thin.

# Rr

R is for Robert, Richard and Rose
Who danced up a rainbow on their toes.

# Ss

S is for Simon, Sadie and Sue
Who sailed in a sandal when the wind blew.

# Tt

T is for Tina, Thomas and Ted
Who taught a tiger to stand on its head.

# Uu

U is for Ulwin and Ursula too
Who bought an umbrella and away they flew.

# Vv

V is for Vera, Vivian and Vance
Who saw a volcano and ripped their pants.

# Ww

W is for Wendy, Wanda and Will
Who worked a windmill on top of a hill.

# X x

X is for Xerxes and Xanthe , it's true
Who played a xylophone, shiny and new.

# Yy

Y is for Yolanda and Yvette
Who ate fruit yogurt, cool and wet.

# Zz

Z is for Zoe, Zara and Zack
Who went to the zoo and never came back.

z                                                                    z

z                                                                    z

# Aa

# Bb Cc Dd Ee

# Ji Kk Ll Mm

# Rr Ss Tt Uu

# Ff  Gg  Hh  Ii

# Nn  Oo  Pp  Qq

# Vv  Ww  Xx  Yy

   Zz